MANAGEMENT BRIEFINGS
HEALTH & SAFETY

Health and Safety Training

Second Edition

MARK COOPER

FINANCIAL TIMES
MANAGEMENT

FINANCIAL TIMES

MANAGEMENT

LONDON • SAN FRANCISCO
KUALA LUMPUR • JOHANNESBURG

*Financial Times Management delivers the knowledge,
skills and understanding that enable students,
managers and organisations to achieve their ambitions,
whatever their needs, wherever they are.*

London Office:
128 Long Acre, London WC2E 9AN
Tel: +44 (0)171 447 2000
Fax: +44 (0)171 240 5771
Website: www.ftmanagement.com

A Division of Financial Times Professional Limited

First published in Great Britain by Technical Communications 1995
Second edition 1998

ISBN 0 273 63221 3
(ISBN 1 859 53005 2 1st edition)

British Library Cataloguing in Publication Data
A CIP catalogue record for this book can be obtained from the British Library.

10 9 8 7 6 5 4 3 2 1

Printed and bound in Great Britain

The Publishers' policy is to use paper manufactured from sustainable forests.

About the author

Mark Cooper is a chartered engineer by training, and joined Aston University's Health and Safety Unit in 1992, having previously worked as a Senior Training Advisor with the Engineering Industry Training Board.

Dr Cooper's recent research includes assessing the quality of training materials supplied to the engineering industry. He is also interested in methods for evaluating the effectiveness of health and safety training for managers and supervisors and in training for dangerous occupations.

If you wish to contact the author please write to the following address:

Health and Safety Unit
Division of Mechanical and Civil Engineering
Aston University
Aston Triangle
Birmingham
B4 7ET

Contents

List of abbreviations   ix

Acknowledgement   x

Introduction   xi

1 Training as a barrier to danger   1
    Background   2
    Training of young people   2
    Commitment to training   3
    Activity and attitudes   4
    Summary   6

2 Consequences of not training   7
    The role of training in changing human behaviour   8
    Other factors affecting behaviour   9
    Human reliability assessments   10
    Human error   10
    Error classification   11
    Accident statistics as a measure of performance   13
    Accident investigation   14
    Preconditions for failure   17

3 Legal requirements   19
    Health and Safety at Work etc. Act 1974   20
    Approved codes of practice   20
    Management of Health and Safety at Work Regulations 1992   22
    Provision and Use of Work Equipment Regulations 1992   23
    Competence   23

4 Training as a risk control measure   26
    Reasons for training   27
    Health and safety culture   27
    Behaviour   28
    Managing risks   30
    Hierarchy of control   32
    The training cycle   33

5	**Mechanisms for identifying training needs**	34
	Induction training	35
	Appraisal and performance review	39
	Continuous professional development	40
	Audits	40
	New work practices	40
	Versatility/multi-skilling	41
	Succession planning and labour turnover	43
6	**Getting started**	46
	The training system	47
	Training planning	48
	Training methods	51
	Training evaluation	53
	Initial status review	55
7	**Summary**	56
	Key points	57
	Training planning	57
	Action plan	57
	Appendices	59
	A Induction training programme – a checklist	60
	B Training plan – pro forma	62
	C Versatility chart – pro forma	63
	D Succession plan – pro forma	64
	E Programme evaluation – end-of-course questionaire	65
	References	68

List of abbreviations

ACOP   approved code of practice

ACSNI   Advisory Committee on the Safety of Nuclear Installations

CDM   Construction, Design and Management Regulations 1994

CPD   continuous professional development

EHO   environmental health officer

FLT   fork lift truck

FTA   fault tree analysis

GWRA   general workplace risk assessment

HRA   human reliability assessments

HSC   Health and Safety Commission

HSE   Health and Safety Executive

HSW   Health and Safety at Work etc. Act 1974

IOSH   Institution of Occupational Safety and Health

ITBs   Industrial Training Boards (these were set up in the UK by the 1964 Industrial Training Act and were broadly responsible for training within their own industry sectors)

MAFF   Ministry of Agriculture, Fisheries and Foods

MCI   Management Charter Initiative

MHSW   The Management of Health and Safety at Work Regulations 1992

NEBOSH National Examining Board in Occupational Safety and Health

NVQ   National Vocational Qualifications

PPE   personal protective equipment

PUWER   Provision and Use of Work Equipment Regulations 1992

TEC   Training and Enterprise Council

QRA   quantified risk assessment

YTS   Youth Training Scheme

Acknowledgement

Examples of best practice in Chapter 5 are reproduced by kind permission of Asda Stores.

Introduction

Aims

The purpose of this management briefing is to enable readers to:

- review the role of training in the achievement of successful health and safety management.

Objectives

After completing this management briefing, readers should be able to:

- describe and discuss the extent to which safe behaviour can be promoted by systematic training;
- discuss the place of training in robust systems for the attainment of health and safety;
- evaluate the role and effectiveness of training in the achievement and maintenance of competency in a given task.

Related competencies

Having read the briefing, and after appropriate practice and experience, the reader will be able to:

- analyse health and safety training needs and develop health and safety training strategies.

Target audience

This management briefing aims to offer practical help to line managers and supervisors who need to manage their resources safely.

The book looks at the reasons why training can improve health and safety performance and shows how training fits into a systematic approach to health and safety management.

Other readers may be personnel managers, company secretaries and general managers of small to medium-sized firms operating in low-risk environments.

The newly appointed safety practitioner may also be a reader, especially if they are studying the NEBOSH (National Examining Board in Occupational Safety and Health) National Diploma or similar qualification.

1

Training as a barrier to danger

Background 2

Training of young people 2

Commitment to training 3

Activity and attitudes 4

Summary 6

Background

Some of the practical issues addressed in this book include:

- identifying safety training needs;
- identifying opportunities for training interventions;
- selecting commonly found off-the-shelf training solutions.

Training of young people

In the mid-1980s the Youth Training Scheme (YTS) was introduced in the UK to tackle the growing problem of youth unemployment. The scheme was initially to last for one year, but it was subsequently extended to two years. In the early days of YTS, it is probably fair to say that the quality of the scheme varied greatly from employer to employer. As a result of a number of well publicised fatalities, all the training providers realised that they had a duty of care towards trainees on their schemes. This resulted in the industry having to rethink its whole approach to the health and safety provisions for its schemes.

Apprenticeships

To take engineering as an example, new entrants to the industry underwent a 36-week period of off-the-job training in approved centres followed by supervised workplace experience. The skills taught varied greatly and took in over 70 recognised trades, ranging from toolmaking to electrical maintenance. Then known as standards-based training, it now forms an integral part of vocational, competence-based craft training. The scheme was administered by the relevant statutory training body, the Engineering Industry Training Board.

Having seen the hazardous environment of engineering workshops, the value of off-the-job training is self-evident. Training carried out in this manner allows three levels of risk control:

- separation of trainees from production pressures;
- provision of competent supervision; and
- effective training.

These measures are valuable in the control of risks and form part of a hierarchy adopted in successful health and safety management. However, it is worth saying that industrial accidents occurring on government training schemes remains a problem.

Commitment to training

It is commonly believed that effective training is an essential element in successful health and safety management. This principle is embedded in UK legislation. Employers, employees and trade unions all agree with, and support, health and safety training. Some typical comments are as follows:

> *Organisations change because people in them learn. Without training there is no learning. Without learning there is no change. Without change there is no profit and without profit there is no business.*
> **Astley Whittall, CBE,**
> **Chairman of Ransome, Sims & Jefferies.**

> *The manager who is trained to know how vital training is, has acquired the most valuable management technique of all.*
> **Bill Jordan,**
> **President of the Affiliated Engineering Unions.**

The problem is that these espoused values don't always get translated into effective action. It is only after an omission or error that the shortcomings in personal or organisational performance are identified. In this respect, much health and safety training occurs as a result of a failure or accident and at a time of increased vigilance. The following quote illustrates the point:

> *Many of the principles of good training are widely known in management circles, and organisations of high quality will adopt them as part of their explicit policy. Unfortunately, it is also true that organisations may pronounce them publicly, and yet at the operational levels treat them casually. Senior management may fail to realise that this is happening. The true state of affairs only emerges when some disaster occurs: Chernobyl,* Herald of Free Enterprise, *King's Cross and* Challenger, *to name but four examples.*
> **Study Group on Human Factors,**
> **First Report on Training and Related Matters,**
> **Advisory Committee on the Safety of Nuclear Installations.**

This reactive approach needs to be challenged and then managed proactively in the same methodical manner that is applied to other business activities.

Activity and attitudes

Comprehensive studies of the nature of health and safety training in the UK across a range of industry sectors do not exist. But as a benchmark (which I also believe reflects the true situation regarding health and safety training), the most recent and comprehensive survey was that published in 1989. The report, *Training in Britain – A Study of Funding, Activity and Attitudes* (Training Agency, 1989), was quite revealing. It identified the following:

- One in five employers reported that they had not carried out any training in 1986/87.

- Of these, 42 per cent reported that they only recruited people who were already experienced rather than train new or existing employees.

- Those that did train, provided training to 48 per cent of their employees.

- Only 24 per cent of companies had a training plan; less still (15 per cent) evaluated the benefits of training.

- Only one in forty companies attempted any cost-benefit analysis of training.

Within those companies that did train in 1986, the average annual amount of training per employee was 14.5 working days. In the health service, the average amount of training per employee was 17.6 days, with 78 per cent of employees receiving training of an average duration of 22.5 days. This was the sector giving the greatest amount of employee training – not surprising, given the life-threatening consequences of human error.

The sector giving the lowest amount of training to its employees was construction. The construction industry is notorious for having a poor safety record and low levels of training. For comparison purposes, Table 1.1 shows the amount of training carried out in the nine industry sectors examined by the study, *Training in Britain – A Study of Funding, Activity and Attitudes*.

Another finding was that the most commonly perceived influence on training was the need to sharpen competitiveness (56 per cent). This was followed by government legislation (40 per cent) – and included health and safety regulations.

Table 1.1
Training activity in different UK industries, 1986–87

Sector	Days per employee	% of employees trained	Days per trained employee
Health	17.6	78	22.5
Education	9.6	64	15.2
Central government	9.5	59	14.3
Retail	8.3	68	12.2
Finance	8.0	52	15.5
Electrical engineering	7.3	40	18.2
Mechanical engineering	6.3	36	17.7
Catering	6.3	45	13.9
Construction	5.8	24	23.8

Source: Training Agency (1989).

This was particularly strong in manufacturing, where it was mentioned by 50 per cent of establishments compared with 36 per cent overall.

The third most influential factor (35 per cent) was the YTS and other government training initiatives. The construction, retail, catering and service industries were particularly influenced by the YTS. By contrast, Industrial Training Boards were mentioned by only one in eight employers in those industries that they serve. Employers cited ITBs as a significant influence to the following extent: construction 24 per cent, engineering 20 per cent and catering 16 per cent.

While the survey did establish the reasons why companies need to train, it did not ask employers the question: 'What stops you from training?' There is a subtle difference between the two. One identifies the catalysts; the other identifies the obstacles. It would have been useful to have had information that either confirmed – or rejected – the anecdotal evidence that flexibility, and the difficulty of releasing key employees from the workplace, are major issues influencing employers' training decisions.

It is important to say that these figures only give the activity levels and are not necessarily an indication of the **effectiveness** of training. Their value lies in helping to locate a firm's position relative to others operating in the same industry sector. Obviously the amount of health and safety training required is related to the risks posed in each industry sector and in each individual premises.

Summary

Training is an important factor in securing a healthy and safe working environment. This is particularly true in areas where there is a perceived low risk or a low degree of supervision. This group includes the self-employed, peripatetic workers (e.g. community nurses, sales representatives, etc.) as well as normally supervised people carrying out unsupervised tasks. It also covers such areas as travel to and from work as well as travel as part of work.

The first point to be made in this book is as follows:

> **In many instances training is the primary barrier protecting employees from danger.**

2

Consequences of not training

The role of training in changing human behaviour 8

Other factors affecting behaviour 9

Human reliability assessments 10

Human error 10

Error classification 11

Accident statistics as a measure of performance 13

Accident investigation 14

Preconditions for failure 17

The role of training in changing human behaviour

One of the complexities of health and safety training is that it is difficult to separate the effects of training from other factors that influence behaviour. It is only in the simplest of cases (for example, sales training) that we can do this. There are a great many other influences that can affect an individual's performance. Two examples are the attitudes of work-colleagues and the culture of the organisation.

The other point to make is that training is a dynamic event. It takes place over a period of time, and the behaviours learned during formal periods of training must be practised. It takes time to do this and during this time-lapse other factors also have an opportunity to affect individuals, e.g. a safety campaign, increased vigilance resulting from a recent accident, a visit from a factory inspector, an imminent audit or a new manager with a vigorous commitment to health and safety.

One way to try to assess the behaviour changes attributable solely to training is to identify two groups of employees. One group, the trained group, will participate in the training. The second group, termed the control, receives no training. It is essential that both groups do identical jobs and are subject to the same everyday influences. This is a similar approach to that used in medical trials for new drugs or new methods of clinical treatment. The only factor that differs between the groups is training and training alone.

Figure 2.1 gives a graphical representation of the method. An arbitrary measure of health and safety performance has been used: the number of documented risk assessments being carried out. The expectation is that the trained group will perform better than the control group after they have received appropriate training.

Figure 2.1
Evaluating training using control groups

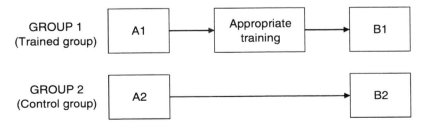

A = Number of documented risk assessments at a date before training
B = Number of documented risk assessments at a date after training

Few situations warrant the use of control groups. Cost and time usually mean that it is not feasible. However, we must be aware of the fact that individual behaviour is influenced by a great many other factors, not just training, and that there are means of separating out their effects.

Other factors affecting behaviour

There are four main factors that affect an individual's performance in the workplace and these are now discussed briefly. The first is to have an adequate selection of individuals for the tasks that have to be performed. Some jobs require, for instance, a large degree of manual dexterity (e.g. electronic assembly work). Others require problem-solving skills (e.g. a process control operator in a chemical factory). Some people are good at these tasks; others are not. Effective selection requires the employee to be correctly matched with the job.

Training is the second factor, and the one that we are going to look at more closely in the remainder of this management briefing. Some of the ways (and this is not a complete list) in which training can be ineffective are:

- the training does not take place at all;
- the training is ill-specified or is inappropriate for the job;
- the trainer is ineffective;
- at the end of training, the expected outcomes/skills are not assessed.

The third requirement is for adequate supervision. This is particularly important in ensuring that the correct standards of work are achieved and then maintained. Good supervision is an essential part of good management.

Lastly, there is the need for adequate employee motivation. Motivation is a complex issue not always solely related to work. Personal and welfare matters can also affect an individual's work performance. **Management vigour** and **example** are thought to be important factors in terms of an individual's motivation towards health and safety issues.

Human reliability assessments

It is important to say that all four of the factors mentioned above must be present if we are to ensure that an individual's performance is to be adequate. Figure 2.2 gives a fault tree showing how a failure of one or more of the four factors leads to inadequate individual performance.

Figure 2.2
Factors leading to inadequate individual performance

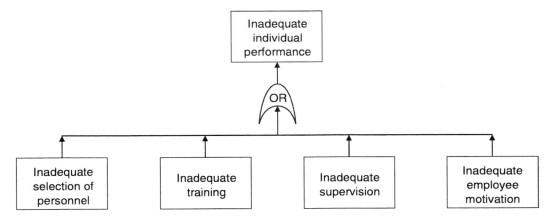

For some safety-critical tasks, it is necessary to evaluate the possible ways in which a human error could lead to danger. It is through an understanding of human behaviour that the risks associated with human error can be assessed. Fault tree analysis (FTA) provides a powerful tool for doing this and is a commonly encountered risk assessment method.

The probability, or chance, of the task being carried out correctly by a human operator is referred to as the **human reliability**. It is usually expressed as a ratio or percentage. A **human reliability assessment (HRA)** is the process of quantifying the degree of certainty that the operator will complete the task successfully.

Human error

Human error is a factor in all accidents. In an authoritative text on the subject, Reason (1986) comments:

> *Error can only be meaningfully applied to planned actions that fail to achieve their desired consequences without the intervention of some chance or unforeseeable agency.*

It is not the purpose of this book to provide a detailed critique of the role of human error in accident causation. However, in the context of training there is one particularly relevant approach to understanding the nature of human error.

Error classification

Slips, lapses and mistakes

Slips and **lapses** may be said to occur where the intended action does not go according to plan. **Mistakes** occur where the plan itself is inadequate to achieve its objectives.

The importance of identifying error types is that each has different characteristics leading to different detection and control strategies. Rasmussen (1974), a distinguished researcher in this area, describes three types or categories of human error: those that are skill-, rule- or knowledge-based.

Skill-based errors

A simplistic view is that slips or lapses are skill-based errors. These errors tend to be related to highly routinised activities in familiar circumstances: omissions, repetitions, reversals, interference errors and double-capture slips (*see* Figure 2.3). Other examples of slips include:

- failing to apply the handbrake on leaving a vehicle (omission);
- failing to disengage the gears before starting the engine (omission).

Training can be used to instil safe practices into habituated work routines.

The next two categories of error are concerned with problem solving.

Figure 2.3
Example of a skill-based error: incorrect use of controls

Fork-lift trucks have a number of different types of foot pedal controls. Some operate with three pedals (as a car). Others have two pedals – reverse and forward. Removing a foot from either accelerator brings the vehicle to a halt.

A common error is for the driver to press the backwards accelerator in the belief (wrongly) that it is a brake pedal.

Double-capture slips result from the influence of a recent highly practised routine upon the task at hand, the cause being a **strong habit intrusion**.

Rule-based errors

Rule-based errors are concerned with the misapplication or inappropriate use of problem-solving rules. Individuals have a complex array of specific and general rules that they use to deal with everyday problems. Rules are of the type *if* <event> *then* <action>. Some simplistic examples relating to the operation of vehicles are as follows:

- *If* <machine blockage> *then* <disengage power, switch off engine and investigate>.

- *If* <pallet or stillage insecure> *then* <re-secure>.

- *If* <towing a trailer on slopes> *then* <connect trailer brakes>.

Sometimes our rules are incomplete:

- *If* <emergency> *then* <apply handbrake, switch off engine and dismount>.

This is a perfectly good rule under most circumstances. However, with accidents involving contact with high voltage overhead lines, remaining in the cab provides protection against electrocution (by the principle of the Faraday cage). A better additional rule would be:

- *If* <emergency involving electricity> *then* <stay in cab until supply isolated>.

The role of training in providing individuals with a set of safe rules is crucial.

This is especially true when faced with **counter-intuitive** information. For example:

- Counter-balanced fork-lift trucks are **less** stable when unladen than when laden and the load properly stowed (*see* the example relating to a fork-lift truck fatality on p. 14 below).

Knowledge-based errors

Knowledge-based errors are concerned with performance in novel or new situations. Actions have to be planned 'on-line'. The process is intellectually demanding. The problem-solver will only resort to this type of activity when they have run out of rule-based solutions. An example of knowledge-based performance is that of first learning to operate a piece of machinery.

The hydraulic controls of a back hoe provide a good example. Experimentation will help the operator to build a mental model of how the controls can be co-ordinated to achieve the desired movements. Eventually, the operator will adopt a set of rules derived from that mental model and, with practice, the task will become skill-based. Training offers the opportunity to miss out the experimentation phase by guiding the trainee to correct models of situations, based upon the experiences of others.

Accident statistics as a measure of performance

The traditional approach in health and safety has been to use accident statistics as the primary measure of performance. Although this sounds plausible at first, a little extra thought shows it to be flawed. There is a large number of inadequacies in this approach (Booth, 1994) including the following:

- Failure – not success – is being measured.
- No account is taken of the random fluctuations in events. (If the risk of being killed or seriously injured in a road accident each year is one in ten thousand, would such an accident be just one of the unfortunate, but tolerable, rare events?)
- There is a time lag before it is possible to judge success.
- Chronic, long-term ill-health is not being assessed.
- Comparisons between different industry sectors are difficult. Comparisons are only truly possible against previous years within the same premises and using the same reporting system.

- Evidence of previous failures may not be a predictor of future failures.

- There are limitations in high-consequence, low-probability situations. (For example, is it meaningful for the operators of a nuclear power station to say that they have had only one accident since being commissioned?)

- No assessment of the timeliness and cost-effectiveness of safety effort is made.

- There may be under-reporting of accidents.

For the reasons already discussed, using accident data alone as a measure of safety performance has many drawbacks and inadequacies. Linking the effectiveness of health and safety training to these statistics is over-simplifying the role of training in the complexities of accident causation. At its crudest, this approach implies that providing twice the training activity will produce a reduction in accident statistics of 50 per cent. Clearly this is not true. Under-reporting or inaccurate reporting of accidents will also invalidate the link between accident statistics and training. However, seen alongside other initiatives, training can be seen as **one** contribution to the measurement of safety performance.

Accident investigation

To illustrate the importance of training in the provision of a safe and healthy working environment, the following case studies show the human tragedy and commercial loss that can arise from a failure to train effectively. Both were investigated by the author. Some details have been changed to protect the identity of those involved. Any number of other examples could have been used.

Fork-lift truck fatality

This accident concerns an injury to persons. A young, newly married man in his early twenties was killed while driving his unladen fork-lift truck (FLT). The accident happened on the compacted, coarse aggregate floor of a storage compound. The vehicle, rated at 7.5 tonnes, was being driven unladen a short distance before it overturned. Evidence showed that the vehicle was on full lock at the time and scuff marks on the tyres and skid marks on the floor indicated harsh braking and speed.

Unladen FLTs are in a less stable state than when properly laden and travelling with the forks just off the ground. This is because the heavy counterbalance raises the centre of gravity. When carrying a full load, this counterbalance serves the useful purpose of stopping the vehicle from a longitudinal (tipping forward) overturn.

The large mass needed for the counterweight is positioned in such a way that, when combined with the front load properly stowed, the net effect is to move the overall centre of gravity nearer the ground, making it more stable than when it is unladen.

The technical explanation for the accident was lateral instability resulting from side forces related to the sharp cornering speed and harsh braking. A slight cross-fall at the scene was a minor contributing factor. Like many vehicle stability accidents the operator was killed by becoming trapped under the vehicle as it overturned. It was inconclusive as to whether the operator was thrown from, or was trying to jump clear of, the vehicle as it overturned. The company were successfully prosecuted under s2 of the Health and Safety at Work (HSW) Act for inadequate training and supervision and fined £10 000. Lack of training contributed to the operator failing to appreciate:

- the dangerous combination of speed, harsh braking and sharp cornering;

- the action to be taken in the event of an overturn;

- the importance of routine maintenance;

- the fact that unladen trucks can be less stable than laden ones.

Factory accident: machining centre

This accident was associated with a railway rolling-stock wheel during routine maintenance. The particular type of wheel being machined was referred to as a **mono-block wheel**. The accident investigation centred around the events that took place leading to a wheel leaving the machine very rapidly and landing on the workshop floor some metres away.

The approximate weight of the wheel was 250 kg. The machinery guarding was completely destroyed. One of the jaws (weighing several kilograms) and a number of retaining bolts were also thrown across the shopfloor. Other than the operator suffering mental trauma, there were no injuries to persons.

The operation being carried out at the time was vertical boring. This is where a sharp-tipped tool travels vertically through a rotating workpiece. In this case the machine was reboring the axle housing. The workpiece was being held in place by four jaws mounted around the outer diameter.

A crucial feature of the railway carriage wheel was that it had a tapered wheel edge. As a consequence, the clamping at the jaws was not very effective because the square shape of the jaws met a tapered wheel edge.

On examination it was noted that, typically, one or two of the clamping teeth were missing and therefore the clamping, instead of being on four teeth, was on two or three. The reason why clamping was not over a large number of teeth (e.g. about ten) was because of the tapered shape of the workpiece. Prior to the accident, the machine operator had noticed that there were above average numbers of tool failures for this job.

The accident investigation quickly established that the system for holding the workpiece was ineffective. It was concluded this accident could be put down to **poor workshop practice**. The hazards associated with vertical boring are widely known to engineers and craftsmen and these ought to have been incorporated into the operator's training. There was a failure to appreciate the:

- causes of chatter (low frequency noise caused by movement between the tool and the workpiece);
- importance of rigidity of both machine and workpiece;
- necessity to have the work well secured during the process;
- avoidance of distortion and spring.

The probable sequence of events is shown in Figure 2.4. Like the previous accident this could have been prevented by adequate training and supervision.

Figure 2.4
Factory accident: probable sequence of events

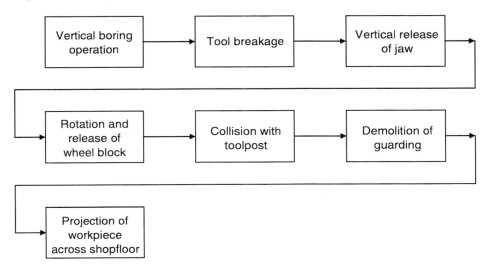

Preconditions for failure

In both of the cases that we have just looked at, one or more preconditions for failure were present. In general, there are four main types of failure: two are technical and two are procedural. All have training implications.

- **Inadequate design for known working conditions**

  These are accidents that are attributable to a design error. An example would be the Flixborough explosion in the UK in June 1976, in which there was a release and subsequent explosion of a vapour cloud of the chemical cyclohexane. The main cause of the accident was poor design control during a temporary plant modification.

- **Actual working conditions different from design**

  This precondition occurs when there are unforeseen design requirements. Arguably, an example of this was the Abbeystead explosion in the UK in 1984 in which 16 people died. An unusual design feature allowed methane to accumulate in the underground water pumping station at Abbeystead. A flammable atmosphere had not been envisaged in the design. The problem of dissolved methane in water supplies was not fully appreciated at that time by civil engineers.

- **Inadequate or ineffective systems of work**

  The roll on/roll off passenger and freight ferry the *Herald of Free Enterprise*,

registered at the port of Dover in the UK, put to sea with its bow doors open. When the ship capsized outside Zeebrugge harbour 188 lives were lost. The main cause was the inadequacy of the system of work for checking that the bow doors were shut.

- **Adequate but unused systems of work**

  The Piper Alpha disaster in which 167 people died was the result of a fire on a North Sea oil platform. A breakdown of the permit-to-work system and of communications at shift changeover were at fault.

Each of these accidents (on whatever scale) represents human and commercial tragedy, with clear training implications for professional designers, managers, supervisors, technicians and operators.

The second point to be made in this book is as follows:

Accident investigation is a very unsatisfactory way of identifying training needs.

3

Legal requirements

Health and Safety at Work etc. Act 1974 20

Approved codes of practice 20

Management of Health and Safety at Work Regulations 1992 22

Provision and Use of Work Equipment Regulations 1992 23

Competence 23

Health and Safety at Work Act 1974

The primary legislation used in the enforcement of health and safety standards in the UK is the Health and Safety at Work etc. Act 1974 (commonly abbreviated to HSW Act). Enforcement is by either the factory inspectorate or by environmental health officers (EHOs). Broadly, EHOs deal with shops and warehouses while Health and Safety Executive (HSE) inspectors deal with the other areas covered by the Act. Specialist HSE inspectors exist for the following sectors: agriculture, railways, offshore, nuclear, explosives, mines and quarries.

The HSW Act arose from the findings of the Robens Report (1972). The Report recommended replacing the 'haphazard and mass of ill assorted and intricate detail' of the then existing legislation with 'a comprehensive and orderly set of revised provisions under a new enabling Act. The new Act should contain a clear statement of the basic principles of safety responsibility.' And so the 1974 Act came into existence. It prescribes general duties imposed on employees and employers (including the self-employed). The most wide-ranging part of the Act is s2 in which it is a general duty 'of every employer to ensure, so far as is reasonably practicable, the health, safety and welfare at work of all his employees'. Essentially this is a restatement of the employer's duties at common law. Of particular interest is s2(c) in which it states that the duty extends to:

> the provision of such information, instruction, **training** [author's emphasis] and supervision as is necessary to ensure, so far as is reasonably practicable, the health and safety at work of his employees.

Clearly there is a fundamental requirement for training in establishing a healthy and safe working environment. This is not a contentious issue, although the specification and the exact requirements in respect of the training provision can be. Establishing the training requirements is generally referred to as **identifying the training need**.

Approved codes of practice

There are certain cases where the law gives direction about the type of health and safety training necessary to meet legal obligations. In these cases, employers only need concern themselves with identifying the broad area of training required and selecting an appropriate but approved supplier of the training.

The first example in this category are those instances where the HSE has issued practical guidance and interpretation of the law in the form of approved codes of practice (ACOPs). ACOPs have a special place in law and are made under the authority of s16 of the HSW Act. Other Acts of Parliament also have associated ACOPs. For example, in the case of pesticides used on farms and smallholdings there is a common interest with the Food and Environment Protection Act and a joint code has been published by the Health and Safety Commission (HSC) and the Ministry of Agriculture, Fisheries and Foods (MAFF). Other examples of areas covered by ACOPs include:

- first aid at work;

- fork-lift truck operation;

- agricultural and non-agricultural pesticide use;

- gas installation.

The second area where training is required by law comes under specific regulations (usually referred to as secondary legislation) made under Acts of Parliament, commonly the Factories Act 1961. Many of these are being, or have been, phased out by the Provision and Use of Work Equipment Regulations (PUWER) 1992:

- mounting of abrasive wheels;

- operation of power presses/woodworking machinery.

Usually the ACOPs indicate the training providers approved to supply training courses. Typically, these are national organisations of known repute and include non-statutory training organisations (NSTOs) for that particular industry sector. In addition to ACOPs, the HSC produces other advice on training in the form of guidance notes and other one-off publications. Examples of the guidance notes that have been produced relate to:

- the training of crane drivers and slingers;

- the safe erection of structures;

- the level of training for technicians making noise surveys;

- time off for the training of safety representatives;

- training for health and safety in the print industry.

Management of Health and Safety at Work Regulations 1992

More recent legislation tends not to be so prescriptive in its detail as the HSW Act but provides the process (of risk assessment) that must be followed. The Management of Health and Safety at Work Regulations (MHSW) 1992 is one of the set of regulations commonly referred to as the 'six-pack'. It is European-derived legislation that is now incorporated into UK law. The underlying principle behind the MHSW Regulations is the need to carry out risk assessments. The requirements for training are given in Regulation 11 and are based on the situations where new or increased risks are likely to occur, specifically:

- on recruitment;

- on transfer or upon taking up new responsibilities;

- on the introduction of new or changed work equipment;

- on the introduction of new technology;

- on the introduction of new or changed systems of work.

The need for programmes of training and development that go beyond induction training is clearly recognised. Regulation 11(3)(c) specifies that the training must be:

- repeated periodically;

- be adapted to take account of any new or changed risks;

- take place during working hours.

Personal experience suggests that there are many instances where individuals receive comprehensive training and instruction upon first appointment but thereafter have limited refresher training and continuous professional development (CPD). Engineers are perhaps typical of this group, although the Engineering Council is actively trying to change this culture within its constituent institutions. Other professional bodies are also taking this issue seriously. One of the better of these is the Institution of Occupational Safety and Health (IOSH). In order to maintain corporate membership, members need to be able to demonstrate that they undertake ongoing professional training of adequate quantity and quality. We will return to these issues when considering mechanisms for identifying training needs in Chapter 5.

Provision and Use of Work Equipment Regulations 1992

In addition to Regulation 11 of the MHSW Regulations, employers are required to provide specific training on the use of work equipment. Regulation 9 of PUWER makes two requirements. The first is that employees should receive adequate training in the use of work equipment and any risks arising, and the precautions to be taken. The second is that employers are obliged to train those involved in managing and supervising the use of work equipment.

PUWER revokes some of the older prescriptive legislation relating to sprecific equipment, for example, the Agricultural (Power Take-Off) Regulations, 1957 (as amended) and the Agricultural (Stationary Machinery) Regulations 1959. However, it is important to say that some specific regulations remain, in particular the detailed training requirements in the Abrasive Wheels Regulations 1970 and the Woodmaking Machines Regulations 1974.

Competence

In common usage the term 'competent' has a very loose meaning and is usually associated with the skilled trades. More recently it has acquired a new meaning in relation to vocational qualifications. In health and safety law it has a specific, and legal, meaning that has come about through statute and case law.

A number of regulations specifically require that a competent person carry out specific tasks. Through case law, the courts have decided on the attributes required of a competent person.

Statute

For example, the statutory requirements for the safe operation and use of lifting equipment, including cranes, hoists and lifts, can be found in the Construction (Lifting Operations) Regulations 1961 made under the Factories Act 1961.

Two related regulations specify that a competent person must carry out a regular weekly inspection of mobile cranes and that a safe load indicator should be fitted and maintained:

Regulation 10

....as far as the construction permits be inspected at least once in every week by the driver, if competent for the purpose, or other competent person.

Regulation 30

No mobile crane having either a fixed or derricking jib shall be used unless it is fitted with an approved type of safe load indicator which shall be properly maintained. The indicator shall be inspected in any case at intervals not exceeding one week by the person required under... Regulation 10...

A more recent example is the Pressure Systems and Transportable Gas Containers Regulations 1989. The technical demands of the competent person vary with the size and complexity of the pressure system. With this in mind, the ACOP gives additional guidance on the professional qualifications and duties expected of the competent person. The Guidance on the Regulations, HS(G) 30, goes on to state that:

These Regulations break new ground in the role they give to the 'competent person'. Past legislation gave to competent persons the role of carrying out periodic thorough examination of plant and equipment so as to assess its continuing integrity and fitness for use until the next examination...In addition...the competent person is required to draw up or certify as suitable a written scheme of examination.

Case law

In many ways the Pressure Systems Regulations incorporate the key decisions already established in case law. Two important cases have defined the courts' interpretation of 'competent'. The first is *Gibson v Skibs A/S Marina* (1966) All ER 476 where it was decided, for the purposes of the Factories Act (Docks, Building and Engineering Construction etc.) Modification Regulations 1938, that:

A 'competent person' is one who is a practical and reasonable man, who knows what to look for and how to recognise it when he sees it.

At issue was the requirement in Regulation 14 that no lifting plant be used

...without first being suitably tested by a competent person except in the case of a rope sling manufactured from rope which has been tested by a competent person and spliced in a safe manner.

This is quite a loose definition. In effect, it says that a competent person would be obvious to those familiar with the work to be carried out. The implication is that operators can make this decision for themselves. The second stated case puts the onus on the manager to make the judgment. This is the case of *Brasier* v *Skipton Rock Company* (1962) All ER 955 in which it was decided that a competent person is:

> *A man who on fair assessment of the requirement of the task, the factors involved, the problems to be studied and the degree of danger implicit, can fairly, as well as reasonably be regarded by the manager as competent to perform such an inspection.*

Both of these cases still leave room for interpretation, but lead to the next assertion:

> **There are a number of instances where health and safety law dictates the detailed training needs for specific, commonplace, hazardous operations.**

4

Training as a risk control measure

Reasons for training 27

Health and safety culture 27

Behaviour 28

Managing risks 30

Hierarchy of control 32

The training cycle 33

Reasons for training

There are a number of reasons why training makes an important contribution to health and safety performance. The five most important are that training is:

- required by law;

- changes behaviour;

- associated with competence;

- influences safety culture;

- controls risks.

Competence and law have been dealt with in the previous chapter. In my opinion the most important reason for training is its role as a risk control measure. Before looking at this, we will briefly consider the two outstanding matters of 'safety culture' and 'behaviour'.

Health and safety culture

This term, often abbreviated to safety culture, has recently become the buzzword among health and safety practitioners. There are differing views on what precisely is meant by it. Some argue that it is a process of change – getting an organisation to the point where health and safety issues become an integral part of everyday working life. Another view is that it is:

> *...the way we do things around here.*
> **HSE, 1997**

My own opinion is that to achieve a safety culture requires a progressive change brought about in a systematic and planned manner. There are parallels with establishing a quality or a learning culture (this is sometimes referred to as the 'learning company'). The difference is that instead of getting employees to 'think quality' they need also to 'think safety'. The process to bring about this change requires:

- commitment from senior management;

- setting of safety policy and objectives;

- delegation of authority;

- monitoring of the system;

- approval of changes in the system.

This protocol is transparent and applies to the management of any change. Non-health and safety examples of change include:

- yearly hours;

- equal opportunities;

- no smoking policies;

- no alcohol policies;

- removal of racial discrimination.

What is clear is that in the high-risk industries, safety culture has a vital role to play and that the change to a safety culture requires a high commitment to training. A quotation from a report by the Advisory Committee on the Safety of Nuclear Installations (ACSNI) illustrates this succinctly:

> *The main priority for training so far as safety is concerned is the creation of a 'Safety Culture' although the process of technical information will form an important part of the task.*
> **ACSNI, Study Group on Human Factors,**
> **First Report on Training and Related Matters.**

However, to bring about widespread cultural change often necessitates a change in the senior management of an organisation.

Behaviour

Traditionally, behaviour is thought to have three elements: skill, knowledge and attitude. Attitudes present the greatest problem in that they are both difficult to achieve and difficult to assess. The current vogue is for attitude surveys to be used in the belief that people's attitudes are indicative of the individual's underlying belief systems and are assumed to be a proxy of behaviour. This approach presents a number of problems because asking an individual about their attitudes does not guarantee that the actual attitudes will be divulged. This is a typical characteristic of

much behavioural science – by seeking to measure an aspect of human behaviour you are actually distorting the very factor that you are attempting to measure. Some form of intervention is necessary to ascertain the subject's perceptions of a particular situation.

It has been found that in terms of attitudes to health and safety, the predictive factor is not what the subject says their attitudes are, rather it is what the subject **believes their line manager's attitudes to be**. If the subject thinks that their line-manager has a positive attitude to health and safety then that bodes well for the safety culture of the organisation. The converse also applies.

It is widely believed that health and safety training can help to stimulate attitude changes. Some common examples of the sort of behaviour changes that we are trying to effect are:

- hazard spotting;
- accident and near-miss reporting;
- consideration for the safety of others;
- violations of safety systems/procedures;
- employee perceptions of a 'blame culture'.

All of these factors are influenced by training. However, they are also affected by other factors. For instance, production pressures may be overwhelming to the point where violations of safety procedures become inevitable. The role of management in creating and avoiding these conflicting pressures must not be underestimated.

A recurring theme in accident investigation is that, while the operator may have been the actual person to commit the violation, that act is the last in a series of barriers to have been broken, any one of which could have prevented the accident occurring. The true underlying cause is a breakdown of adequate management control of the risks.

A notable example of this is the aircrash in 1989 at Kegworth, Northamptonshire, involving the Airbus 300 series. The cause was said to be pilot error. In fact, a large number of factors brought about the accident, not least of which was the phenomenon of 'turbine flutter' – a form of distortion of the turbine blades which

occurred under certain operating conditions. This brought about a collision between the turbines and their casing in one of the two engines. However, the pilot's decision to shut down the 'wrong' engine was based upon poor instrumentation, particularly in the design and positioning of the engine vibration indicators which had a history of unreliability. Although it has to be said that the digital instruments fitted on the aircraft in question were of an improved design, this did not alter the pilot's perception that they were unreliable. A further factor was the failure of these instruments to be prominently displayed or to have out-of-range markings. Whichever way the crash is considered, the pilot did make errors but these were only as a result of trying to ameliorate far more serious technical and design errors that were latent within the system.

Managing risks

Probably the most important aspect of health and safety training in low-risk situations is as a measure of risk control. A major influence has been the Hale and Glendon model based upon research work into human behaviour in the face of danger (Hale and Glendon, 1987). The model advocates a systematic approach to risk management, the principles of which have been incorporated into the HSE's *Successful Health and Safety Management* HS(G)65 (1997), the authoritative source for guidance on the practicalities of managing risks. A schematic of the approach is given in Figure 4.1.

The five steps to successful health and safety are as follows:

1   **Set policy**

A genuine commitment from senior management is necessary and a clear statement to that effect is vital.

2   **Organising**

This is concerned with getting the systems and procedures in place to achieve the policy objectives. Particular attention needs to be paid to the competence of staff, control of the workforce, co-operation between individuals and functions and effective communication (upwards, downwards and side to side).

Figure 4.1
Model of the systematic approach to risk management

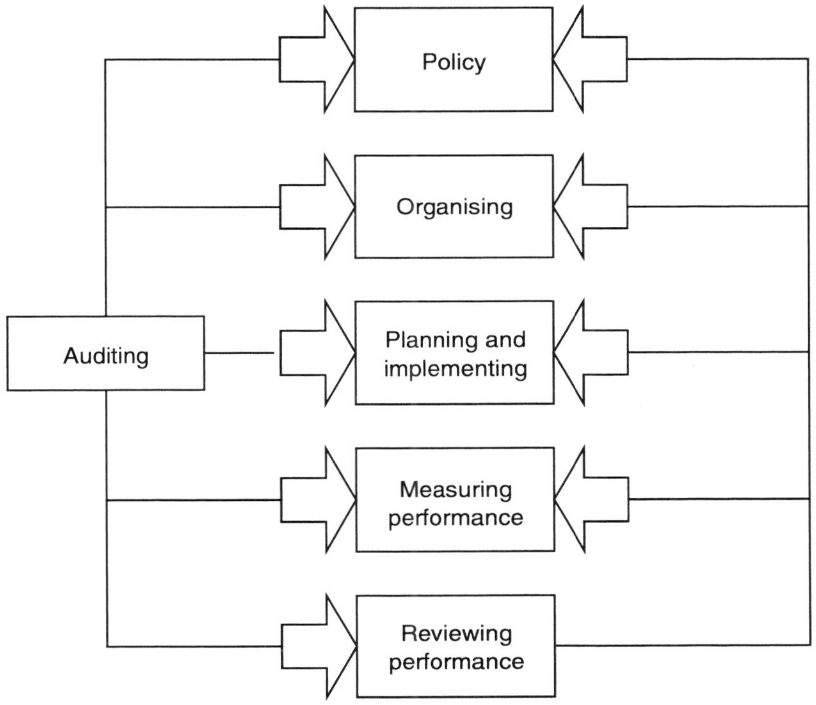

Source: HSE(1997).

3   **Planning and setting standards**

In order to manage health and safety successfully it is necessary to set objectives, identify hazards, assess risks and implement standards of performance. Standards must be measurable, achievable and realistic.

4   **Measuring performance**

An important aspect of managing health and safety is knowing your current status, where you would like to be and deciding the strategy to achieve the difference. Monitoring (which is different from auditing) concerns itself with the process of gathering and analysing health and safety data. This is undertaken either actively (before things go wrong) or reactively (after things go wrong).

5   **Auditing and reviewing**

Audits (internal or external) complement the monitoring process. These examine whether the performance standards and scope of the system are to the required standard. Essentially audits can ascertain, in an objective way, the degree of compliance with which your systems are operated.

Hierarchy of control

Training's main role is at the planning and implementing stage. One aspect of this is the setting of organisational performance objectives. The five-stage approach to hazard identification and risk assessment is:

1   analyse the task;

2   identify the hazards;

3   assess the risks;

4   implement control measures;

5   monitor and review.

An implicit first step in this iterative process is to define areas of responsibility.

The traditional approach to controlling risks involves the use of a hierarchy of control measures (*see* Figure 4.2). Elimination of the hazard is the most preferred form of control, followed by engineering and technical measures. Systems of work (which include training as well as measures such as quality assurance, permits to work, etc.) are next, followed by the least preferred option of the use of personal protective equipment (PPE). Measures that do not require the intervention of the operator take precedence over other measures.

Figure 4.2
Hierarchy of control measures

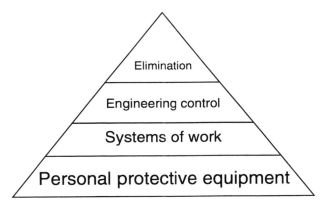

The training cycle

The systematic approach to training that is advocated in HS(G)65 is based upon a widely accepted model of training. More commonly referred to as the training cycle, it comprises four elements: identifying the training need, selecting the training solution, carrying out the training and evaluating the success of the training event (*see* Figure 4.3).

Figure 4.3
The training cycle

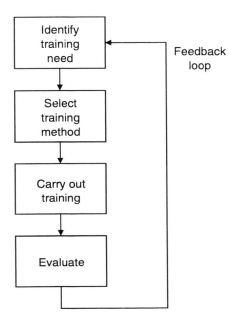

Source: HSE(1997).

This systematic approach is explored in greater depth in the following chapters.

Before proceeding, however, it is important to say that, while training cannot guarantee that the operator will carry out a system of work faultlessly each and every time, it does reduce the chance (or probability) of an undesired event happening. Put simply, it helps to reduce the risk of harm to people or property.

The fourth assertion consequently is as follows:

> **Training is a lower-order measure for controlling risk. However, lower order does not mean unimportant.**

5

Mechanisms for identifying training needs

Induction training 35

Appraisal and performance review 39

Continuous professional development 40

Audits 40

New work practices 40

Versatility/multi-skilling 41

Succession planning and labour turnover 43

Induction training

Induction is by far the most widely practised form of training. Although there has been a tradition of failing to provide training for existing employees in the UK, there has always been strong support for initial or foundation training. This is especially true in the manufacturing industry where craft and technician apprenticeships have a long but declining history. It is worth saying that induction training has great value in trying to control the risks that occur when new employees enter the workplace. With the majority of new entrants being in their late teens, the opportunities that they have had to understand the dangers in the workplace are limited.

Because of its importance we will briefly look at the component parts of an induction training programme. These are thought to be:

- understanding the company;

- terms and conditions of employment;

- disciplinary matters and the grievance procedure;

- customer care;

- general conduct;

- health, safety and welfare issues.

Any induction training programme must give sufficient information for new employees to be able to establish themselves within the organisation. The timeliness of the induction training is critical. Too late and the individual will have ascertained the information in a haphazard manner and feel both frustrated and ignored. Ideally, it should take place within the first week of employment, although the practicalities may mean that this is not always possible.

Selected extracts from a best-practice induction training programme, the ASDA Stores Guide, are shown in Figures 5.1 and 5.2. For example, the Guide gives typical and common workplace hazards. The slips, trips and falls sections are quoted in full in Figure 5.1.

Figure 5.1
Induction training programme: an example of best practice (selected extract)

What is an accident?

'An accident is an unplanned event that leads to injury or damage to people, property or stock.' 'Typical accidents and the way they may be caused are described below.'

Slips

Food debris on the floor.

Rain water in foyer areas.

Ice on the floor of the freezer.

Water spillage or leaks from equipment.

Cardboard or other packaging on the floor.

Oil or grease on the floor.

Plastic bags on the floor.

Ice and snow during winter.

Trips

Protruding parts or fixtures.

Raised flagstones.

Lifting or worn floor coverings.

Electric cables trailing across the floor.

Drawers left open.

Holes in the floor.

Falls

Daleks, ladders, steps and step stools in poor repair or incorrectly used.

Climbing on the racking.

Using the forks of the forklift to lift people to higher levels.

Unprotected edges to high-level working areas e.g. loading dock, mezzanine floor, roof level access points.

Cuts and stabbing

Burns and scalds

Falling objects

Contact with moving vehicles

Exposure to hazardous substances

Electrical contact

Manual handling

Trapping

Source: ASDA Stores Guide.

Figure 5.2
Induction training programme: an example of best practice (selected extract)

ASDA

Your Guide to Personal Safety

Introduction

In ASDA we take health and safety issues seriously. We want you to:

- have a safe and healthy environment in which to work

- be provided with safe materials, equipment and machinery

- receive the necessary information, training and supervision to enable you to work safely.

You have an important part to play in making sure that you and your colleagues do not have an accident at work.

PLEASE ENSURE THAT YOU:

- work in accordance with the training and instructions you have received

- report any defects in the materials, equipment or machinery you use

- report any accidents or 'near misses' that occur involving people, buildings, stock or equipment

- question existing procedures if you feel they can be made even more safe

- refer to your departmental procedures and the health, safety and fire manual for more detailed information.

FOR YOUR OWN SAFETY PLEASE:

DO TAKE SAFETY SERIOUSLY

DO NOT FOOL AROUND WITH EQUIPMENT – USE IT CORRECTLY

DO NOT BE OVER-CONFIDENT

Source: ASDA Stores Guide.

Suggested content of induction training

As part of the free-issue material at the back of this book, there is a checklist for an induction training programme covering these important areas. Not all aspects of the checklist are going to apply to each and every organisation but many of the core elements of an induction programme are common to all types, sizes and sectors of establishments. It is these that have been incorporated into the checklist.

Understanding the company

In many ways, this part of the induction programme is concerned with orienting new employees to their new working environment. This part of the training has to be carried out as soon as possible after joining, otherwise it has no value. By its very nature, this part of the training can be done informally and on an individual basis on the very first day of employment.

Terms and conditions of employment

The general terms and conditions of employment need to be explained to new recruits. Generally speaking, seasoned employees would take these for granted. Payment, working hours, the contract of employment and the period of notice all come under this heading. At the outset it is necessary to explain the correct procedures for clocking in and out (if appropriate) and the company's policy on lateness and any deduction of pay that will result, typically one minute's worth of wages deducted for each minute of lateness. The use of the staff canteen (if applicable) should also be discussed.

Disciplinary matters and the grievance procedure

This is a tricky matter but the company's disciplinary and grievance procedures are best made clear when new employees join the organisation. It is important that employees know the standards of behaviour expected of them and the seriousness with which any violations of company standards are to be treated. This is especially true of safety-related matters such as the removal and defeating of machinery guards, interference with machinery, failure to wear personal protective equipment (PPE), failure to report accidents and near misses, etc.

Customer care

Most large organisations have a dedicated programme of training relating to customer care. For instance, in the retail sector the high degree of customer contact means that virtually all employees have a need for this. However, in smaller companies – particularly in manufacturing – the degree of customer contact is small, possibly limited to just telephone conversations. The standards of performance that are required of employees need to be explained.

General conduct

This part of induction covers the general standards of behaviour that are acceptable and those that are not. Attitudes to alcohol and smoking are important matters. If the company has such policies, then this is the time to discuss them.

Health, safety and welfare issues

Health, safety and welfare issues would normally be integrated into all other parts of the induction programme, but specific hazards associated with the workplace will need to be covered separately. This will include relevant systems of work as well as emergency and evacuation procedures. Matters relating to the security of plant, equipment and property would be covered at this point, as would health screening and surveillance facilities.

Increasingly the problem of personal security is a concern to employees and employers alike. Advice and guidance covering this need to be part of the formal induction programme.

Appraisal and performance review

Another common method for identifying training needs is the appraisal or performance review. It has long been thought that these provide an effective vehicle for identifying training needs, especially for the supervisory and management grades. Obviously this is not their primary purpose but they can be useful aids in establishing a system for identifying the training needs of existing staff.

Continuous professional development

Future goals (as well as improving an employee's existing performance) can be affected positively by the use of training. As mentioned in Chapter 3, the professional status of existing employees needs to be maintained. This can be assured by a systematic approach to staff development. One way of doing this is via the appraisal or performance review process.

Audits

Audits, whether they be for safety or quality, identify non-compliances within the system being audited. Usually these are categorised as critical, major or minor non-compliances. Invariably, training is one of the factors necessary to rectify the problem. Many documented quality assurance systems require organisations to adopt a formal approach to the management of the training function. An advantage of this is that there is then an audit trail that can identify whether an individual has or has not received appropriate training to operate specific machines or processes. It also enables the organisation to offer a robust defence to the excuse '...but nobody ever told me how to do it properly!'

New work practices

New work practices and the purchase of machinery and equipment all have associated training needs (often suppliers provide training as part of the purchasing arrangements). One recent development in health and safety training has been the arrival of quality assurance systems, notably ISO9000/BS5750. One of the key parts of the standard is the need to document systems and procedures, especially those associated with the production and manufacturing operation. The process of deriving written procedures forces an organisation to examine in detail the various elements of each job. There is anecdotal evidence that this can aid the establishment of safer systems of work.

Versatility/multi-skilling

One effect of the recent economic recession has been the need for fewer people to do the same job to the same or higher standards. The consequences of this are that employees have to be much more flexible. A trend originating in America and Japan has been the need for multi-skilling. An example of this is the creation of machine minders who will tackle all the maintenance tasks for that machine whether they be mechanical, electrical or hydraulic in origin.

Slimmed down organisations are vulnerable to staff shortages at times of high rates of absenteeism or illness. One method for identifying potential problems is the versatility chart – sometimes referred to as the skills matrix. The approach is very simple, cross-referencing the abilities of employees with the principal operations of the business. Each individual's capabilities in each operation are mapped out so that it is possible to identify not only the flexibility of particular employees but also those operations or processes where absenteeism could be most damaging.

Experience shows that it is very rare for an organisation to draw up a versatility chart and not identify potential areas of weakness. The benefit is that, having identified these areas, it is then possible to develop contingency plans.

In a crude form, Figure 5.3 shows a basic versatility chart. Notice that a small number of employees are all highly trained and are all capable of working on at least two different machines. Four of the five employees are able to work more than three machines.

The area of weakness is in the operation of machine five; if employee 1 is absent the machine cannot be operated (in a practical situation it is likely that a supervisor would take on this task). The appropriate action here may be to select an individual for more training, perhaps employee 2 because of the similarity of skills with employee 1.

Versatility charts can be refined by adding information about whether operators are in the process of being trained or are earmarked for future training. However, only in the very simplest of cases is it possible for one person to keep accurate track of all this information. Even in the simple example illustrated in Figure 5.3 there are 75 separate pieces of information contained in the matrix.

Figure 5.3
Simple versatility chart

	Machine 1	Machine 2	Machine 3	Machine 4	Machine 5
Employee 1	✔	✔			✔
Employee 2	✔	✔			
Employee 3	✔	✔	✔	✔	
Employee 4		✔	✔	✔	
Employee 5	✔	✔	✔	✔	

✔ Indicates that the employee is adequately trained

Versatility chart – worked example

A fictitious example of the more sophisticated type of chart for operations in a bakery is shown in Figure 5.4. There are a few points to note from this. The area marked as '1' shows that both Joyce and Phyllis are each only fully trained in 4 out of the 11 operations and that they have a very similar range of skills. The area indicated as '2' shows there to be just one employee, Joyce, fully trained in 'shift preparation' and only one partly trained (George). The obvious comment is that this organisation has a weak point here and is vulnerable if Joyce were to be absent. The advice to the company would have to be to improve the flexibility of Joyce and Phyllis by increasing their skills from four to five or even six of the operations. The greatest weakness is in the shift preparation area but they are also weak on doughnut jamming.

The conclusion is that increased flexibility could be achieved by broadening Phyllis and Joyce's range of skills and by fully training Eileen and George in doughnut jamming.

As part of the free-issue material with this publication there is a blank versatility chart for your use.

Figure 5.4
Sample versatility chart

	Doughmaking	Tinning	Doughnut frying	Oven take-off	Creaming	Despatch	Doughnut jamming	Traying-up	Bun finishing	Patisserie finishing	Shift preparation	
Edna	✔	✔	✔	✔	◆	✔				◆		
Phyllis				*1*		✔	✔	✔	✔	◆		
Joyce								✔	✔	✔	✔	*2*
Eileen		◆		✔	✔	✔	◆	✔				
Fred	✔	✔	✔	✔		✔						
George	✔	✔	✔	✔		✔	◆	◆	◆	◆	◆	

Key
◆ Partly trained
✔ Fully trained

Succession planning and labour turnover

Natural wastage of staff is a fact of life. Retirements, ill-health, job transfers and promotions all mean that staffing levels can never remain static. In some industries labour turnover can reach very high rates. Instances of 15 per cent turnover per year have been found among assembly workers in the domestic electronic goods market. While these rates are very high, the work is mundane and largely appeals to younger employees looking for an entry into the jobs market. Within a couple of years they move on.

It is difficult to predict exact rates of wastage but most firms have an inkling of the magnitude of their particular turnover rates. It must also be said that the recent economic climate has depressed the rates of staff turnover.

In terms of predicting where the losses are likely to occur, the two areas of most interest are those just entering and those about to leave the jobs market. It is by

balancing these that a steady flow of new talent replaces those who are retiring. It is necessary to plan for there to be an overlap between the recruitment of replacement staff and the retirement of the leavers. In this way the skills of the existing employees are passed on to their replacements in an ordered way. An essential ingredient of this handover period is effective training for the replacements. It is through succession planning that we have the opportunity both to recruit and to train for future losses of employees.

Most succession planning is based upon identifying those areas of the business that involve the greatest degree of skill and knowledge and the anticipated losses over the following three to five years. Particular attention must be paid to two areas. First, estimating the number of retirements (the major cause of natural wastage) and, second, determining the required number of skilled employees required to take the replacement of leavers. The point at which employees will need to be recruited must take account of the length of time taken to train these employees to the required standard.

Worked example

A worked example of a succession plan is shown in Figure 5.5. Two areas are marked. The first shows that this company has a large proportion of its semi-skilled workers in the under-25 age group, accounting for 39 of the 182 employees (21 per cent). The second area shows that 20 of the 58 employees in the over-45s are managers. The number of young people (less than 25 years), of which there are 49, is similar in size to the number of older employees (the 43 who are over-50). There are no particular points to make other than that the number of potential managers (current supervisors) who are under 40 years of age is quite small (nine in all) and that the company needs to be aware that this is a potential source of future managers.

The concluding observation from this chapter is as follows:

Appraisals, auditing, succession planning and the introduction of new work practices (e.g. multi-skilling) are just a selection of the methods available to employers for identifying health and safety training needs.

Figure 5.5
Sample succession plan

Age / Function	Total	16	17	18	19	20	21	22	23	24	25–9	30–4	35–9	40–4	45–9	50–4	55	56	57	58	59	60
Manager	(29)	0	0	0	0	0	0	0	0	0	1	2	3	3	4	5	4	2	3	1	1	0
Supervisors	(25)	0	0	0	0	0	0	0	0	0	1	3	5	7	5	3	0	0	1	0	0	0
Chargehands	(13)	0	0	0	0	0	0	0	0	0	1	3	4	2	1	2	0	0	0	0	0	0
Maintenance	(4)	0	0	0	0	0	0	1	0	1	1	0	0	1	0	0	0	0	0	0	0	0
Fitters	(3)	0	1	0	0	0	0	0	0	0	1	1	0	0	0	0	0	0	0	0	0	0
Kitchen staff	(9)	2	1	0	1	0	1	0	3	0	0	0	0	0	0	0	0	0	1	0	0	0
Cleaners	(7)	0	0	0	0	0	0	0	0	0	0	0	0	0	2	1	1	0	2	0	0	0
Security	(2)	0	0	0	0	0	0	0	0	0	0	0	0	0	1	1	0	0	0	0	1	0
Production	(10)	0	0	0	0	0	0	0	0	0	0	5	2	2	1	0	0	0	0	0	0	0
Assembly	(80)	12	9	8	0	5	2	0	3	0	13	15	0	0	1	5	2	2	1	1	3	0

1

2

6

Getting started

The training system 47

Training planning 48

Training methods 51

Training evaluation 53

Initial status review 55

The training system

It is hoped that it is clear from previous comments that there is more to effective health and safety training than simply sending people on courses. In fact, there are two important constituent parts. First, there is the system for identifying the training needs and for proposing solutions (generally referred to as 'training planning'). Second, there are the actual solutions themselves, the specific learning or training events. As we shall see, there are usually a number of alternative solutions to satisfying training, one of which may be the use of external courses.

It is widely believed that training can be an *ad hoc* activity, undertaken at short notice to 'plug a gap'. Nothing could be further from the truth as far as **effective** training is concerned. In an authoritative textbook (Harrison, 1989), training is described as 'the shorter-term, systematic process through which an individual is helped to master defined tasks or areas of skill and knowledge to predetermined standards'. While this might seem an appealing definition, it does have limitations. In particular, it omits the concept of attitude. This has the least effect in manufacturing and industrial training where the need is predominantly to train for psychomotor skills. It is not true in occupational health and safety where attitudes are of vital importance. A better description is:

> *Training* is the modification of attitudes, knowledge or skill to achieve predetermined standards through a planned process of instruction and practice.

This definition combines the 'skills, knowledge and attitude' approach with that of 'instruction followed by practice'. From what has been said so far, it can be implied that training has the following characteristics:

- It has a target audience (the trainees).
- It modifies knowledge, skills or attitude.
- It is planned.
- It is instruction followed by practice.
- It leads to competence.
- It meets an identified need.

An acceptable way of expressing an organisation's training need is through a **training plan**.

Training planning

Training planning is concerned with answering the following four questions about an organisation's health and safety training:

- Where are we now?

- Where would we like to be?

- How are we going to get there?

- How do we continue to stay there?

The format of the training plan can be very simple, often requiring no more than a statement on a single sheet of paper. A training plan is characterised by the fact that it:

- prioritises the training to be carried out, typically into the categories of **critical**, **major** or **minor priority** (the terminology will be familiar to those who have had any involvement in quality assurance systems);

- sets achievable deadlines for the completion of the training;

- details the period for which it applies and the employees that it covers;

- identifies **in sufficient detail** the type of training needed, for whom it is required and the preferred method of training.

An example of a training plan for a medium-sized business is shown in Figure 6.1. One point to note is that the quantified risk assessment is required only by a few individuals and is obviously dependent upon the nature and complexity of the business. In short, it will be determined by the hazards associated with the product or process. Many of the items that will appear on a health and safety training plan are what may be called 'off-the shelf' solutions. Some examples are discussed below .

Health and safety practitioners

An accepted route here is for the individual to undertake the NEBOSH two-part National Diploma or an equivalent. This is a postgraduate level course and is usually completed as part of the foundation training of newly appointed health and safety managers. The course covers the four main areas of law, risk management,

Figure 6.1
Sample training plan

Employee name	Position held	Training need	Training methodology	Priority	Estimated duration and cost	Target for completion
A	Design Engineer	Quantified risk assessment	Professional conferences and seminars	Minor	5 days in total (£1500)	18 months
B	Safety officer	Foundation programme of professional competency	External course: NEBOSH two-part National Diploma	Critical	30 days in total (£3500)	3–6 months
C	Occupational nurse	First aid at work course	External course	Major	4 days (£400)	6 months
D	Occupational physician	Recent developments in occupational asthma	Seminar	Major	1/2 day (£500)	6 months
E	Production supervisor	General workplace risk assessments	Internal course	Major	1 day (£350)	6 months
F	General manager	Managing safely	External course: IOSH Managing Safely	Major	5 days (£1000)	6 months
G	Personnel and training officer	Introduction to occupational health and safety	External course: NEBOSH National Diploma (Part 1)	Major	5 days (£1000)	6 months

occupational health and safety technology. In addition there is a case study to consolidate the individual topics.

Many employers support their employees to undertake block release for periods of residential study. There are a number of training providers who offer this programme, but the costs of training can run into a couple of thousand pounds, plus the cost of accommodation and subsistence. A smaller number of providers offer more flexible programmes of study including part-time and distance learning.

Personnel and training staff

In smaller organisations it may not be justified to have a full-time health and safety officer and others, often personnel and training, assume responsibility for the health and safety function. In these instances the depth of knowledge required is less than that for a practitioner. Introductory courses (of typically one-week's duration) are available to meet this need.

Junior and middle managers

All managers have at least some responsibility for health and safety. Management competencies include the need for managers to be able to manage safely. In the UK, the body responsible for setting the standards for management training is the Management Charter Initiative (MCI).

To meet these health and safety training needs, IOSH has developed the 'Managing Safely' programme. This has a taught element which is followed by practical assignments in the workplace, thus giving the opportunity to practise and become competent in the skills learned during the taught component of the programme.

Engineers, professional and technical staff

Best practice among the professions is to provide staff with updating training. This can take the form of a professional conference or seminar. There is a growing awareness of the need to keep up to date with new work practices and is certainly true in the area of quantified risk assessment (QRA). Most training needs for the common risk assessment techniques can be satisfied. The same cannot be said for general workplace risk assessment (GWRA) although a number of computer

programs exist for guiding employers through a semi-quantitative risk assessment (this is the idea of a simple risk calculator). As European legislation becomes ingrained into everyday practice there will be a growing need for training solutions to meet the requirements of the display screen, manual handling and other regulations. In particular, the adoption of risk assessment as an everyday task will have far-reaching consequences for all types and sizes of business.

Training methods

In previous chapters we have said that the training needs of different groups can be met in a variety of ways. Various methods of training exist which need to be used selectively in order to cater for the individual needs of learners. Some examples of training methods are as folllows:

On-the-job:

- 'sitting by Nellie' (*see* below)
- instruction
- supervision
- coaching
- work shadowing.

Off-the-job:

- flexible
- conventional
- open
- text-based
- computer-based
- interactive video
- seminars
- video-led
- audio.

It is fair to say that a large number of employers underestimate their training activity by not including on-the-job training in their assessments. On-the-job training means more than just letting an individual loose on a particular job.

The above methods of on-the-job and off-the-job training are self-explanatory, although inappropriate selection of delivery media is a common cause of unsuccessful training. While sophisticated media such as computer-based training and interactive videos **do** have their place, the general advice is to keep it simple wherever possible.

Evidence from research carried out into the quality of open learning materials supplied to the engineering industry showed that sophisticated delivery media did not guarantee a quality product. An extract from a recent publication of the research reads as follows:

> *A range of 67 products, in eight subject areas and from 39 suppliers, were evaluated. The majority (48) were either text-based (32) or video-led (16). The remainder (19) were audio, computer-based training (CBT) and interactive video (IV) packages. Three main findings emerged from the research. Firstly, that price alone is not a predictor of quality. Secondly, good quality products exist across the entire price range including some at less than £50. Thirdly, text-based materials formed the majority of the good quality products (24 out of 34), followed by video-led (5) and interactive video (4).*
> **Cooper (1995).**

The most appropriate method of training will depend on many factors, the most common of which are:

- skill and knowledge content;
- ease with which key employees can be released from the workplace;
- degree of instruction and practice required to become proficient;
- time available for the training;
- availability of tutors;
- cost;
- viable numbers.

Often there are a number of suitable solutions. If this is so, then cost and convenience become deciding factors. An increasingly important factor is the release

of key employees. This is best illustrated by a quote from a training manager of a large manufacturing company in the West Midlands:

I've never had a request for training being turned down on the basis of cost alone. But I have had a request turned down because key employees could not be released from the workplace.

By far the most common method for on-the-job training is the use of an experienced employee to show trainees 'the way we do it here'. The most widely used term which, although bordering on the politically incorrect, refers to this type of training as 'sitting by Nellie'. While not a very sophisticated method it is very effective. To a large degree its success depends on the correct selection of 'Nellie'. Desirable attributes (not in any particular order of importance) are:

- experience of the particular task/job for which training is being given;
- experience in instructional techniques;
- perceived seniority among workmates;
- friendly and approachable manner;
- patience;
- nurturing and caring skills;
- age – youth sometimes being a disadvantage.

Training evaluation

So far, very little has been said about evaluation. This is because evaluation can only be carried out once the training system is up and running. It is important to say that sophisticated evaluation techniques do exist, but it would be pointless to establish them when the basic training system is not up and running.

As previously mentioned, very few organisations undertake even rudimentary evaluations. The pragmatic approach to evaluation is to try to answer the question: 'Would we do this training the same way next time?' Some of the answer will come from the manager responsible for commissioning the training, some will come from the trainees themselves. It is well established that the reactions of trainees to their course is an important factor in evaluating any training programme. Over the years,

trainers have developed a range of methods for this sort of evaluation. The two most popular (and the ones that are operated at the Aston training programmes) are the end-of-course questionnaire and the course review session.

End-of-course questionnaires

Sometimes referred to as happiness sheets, these are usually tick-box sheets for delegates to complete at the end of their training sessions. Delegates are asked to provide a graded response to the questions, the grades usually ranging from highly satisfied to dissatisfied. There is a choice as to whether they are anonymous or not, although higher response rates can be expected from the anonymous questionnaires. Typically, questions would relate to:

* content and relevance of the session;

* quality of course handouts;

* balance of the course;

* clarity of objectives;

* quality of overheads (if appropriate) and other visual aids;

* adequacy of syndicate and group exercises;

* accommodation (if appropriate);

* food;

* refreshments.

A standard evaluation form, developed from one originally devised by the author's colleague, Roger Clarke, is in the free-issue material.

Review sessions

A very useful form of evaluation is to give trainees the opportunity to discuss with the whole group their views of the training. This has a number of advantages, particularly for programmes that are quite long in duration. With very short courses it is not worthwhile. A few dangers exist in that the group's views can be distorted by a few dominant individuals. It is a very open way of seeking honest views but can run the risk of being 'a free for all' if not managed properly.

Initial status review

When establishing a new training system the hardest job is carrying out an initial status audit. Quite clearly the very first review of the system will reveal shortcomings – that is its purpose. Doing so can be a disheartening job because it reveals the very worst situation that is likely to be found when the system is not properly up and running.

One of the questions that is most likely to arise is 'precisely what legislation applies to us?' For a small enterprise this question can usually be answered quite simply. If in doubt, this is an area where some outside expertise may be helpful. Health and safety consultants may be an overkill but should not be excluded, especially if the operation or process is known to be hazardous. The best advice is to contact your local Training and Enterprise Council (TEC) or local Enterprise Agency and seek their advice. Larger practices of commercial solicitors also now provide advice to employers on legal requirements.

A failure to correctly identify the key training issues can undermine subsequent well-intentioned efforts. This leads to the final assertion in this book:

> **To be effective, training must be planned, meet an identified need, have a target audience and lead to competence. Instruction must be followed by practice.**

7

Summary

Key points 57

Training planning 57

Action plan 57

Key points

- In many instances training is the primary barrier protecting employees from danger.

- Accident investigation is a very unsatisfactory way of identifying training needs.

- There are a number of instances where health and safety law dictates the detailed training needs for specific, commonplace, hazardous operations.

- Training is a lower-order measure for controlling risk. *However, lower order does not mean unimportant.*

- Appraisals, auditing, succession planning and the introduction of new work practices (e.g. multi-skilling) are just a selection of the methods available to employers for identifying health and safety training needs.

- To be effective, training must be planned, meet an identified need, have a target audience and lead to competence. Instruction must be followed by practice.

Training planning

Training planning is concerned with answering the following four questions about an organisation's health and safety training:

- Where are we now?

- Where would we like to be?

- How are we going to get there?

- How do we continue to stay there?

Action plan

- Carry out a training needs analysis.

- Develop a training plan.

- Secure a training budget.

- Review frequently.

Carry out a training needs analysis

Identify the team or individual that will do this. Key requirements of the team are:

- knowledge of the business;

- awareness of current health and safety legislation.

In smaller organisations this may be left to one person – probably you! This is the stage at which you should do an initial status review.

Develop a training plan

It is important to prioritise the training that needs to be carried out. A training plan also allows budgeting for training in subsequent financial plans. It is vital that the health and safety expertise is available at this stage. It is likely that this will be the area where the first training that will need to be carried out and is obviously a high priority. Some organisations buy in specialist advice. This is no substitute for having a competent person on the premises.

Secure a training budget

This is essential. Although in the short term it may be difficult to secure a budget, commitment from the senior management in the organisation is vital. It may be that this is the most difficult task of all.

Review frequently

When 'jump-starting' the system it may be necessary to review progress on a very frequent basis (fortnightly or monthly in the first instance). As progress is made this can be a quarterly exercise.

Good luck!

Appendices
Free-issue material

A   Induction training programme – a checklist 60

B   Training plan – pro forma 62

C   Versatility chart – pro forma 63

D   Succession plan – pro forma 64

E   Programme evaluation – end-of-course questionaire 65

Appendix A
Induction training programme –
a checklist

Understanding the company *Tick box*

THE COMPANY

History ☐

Market sector ☐

Company structure ☐

Company mission ☐

Commitment to quality ☐

BENEFITS

Staff social club ☐

Staff discount ☐

Share participation ☐

Pension scheme ☐

Death benefits ☐

STAFF DEVELOPMENT

How your performance is measured ☐

Your training and development ☐

Terms and conditions of employment

PAY

Written contract ☐

Method and date of payment ☐

Tax and wages queries ☐

Overtime ☐

Sick pay ☐

PUNCTUALITY

Procedures for clocking in and out ☐

Deductions for lateness ☐

Procedures in the event of sickness ☐

MATERNITY

Pay ☐

Leave ☐

OTHER

Union membership ☐

Disciplinary matters and grievance procedure

Misconduct/Gross misconduct (examples) ☐

Theft ☐

Spot checks ☐

Invoking the grievance procedure ☐

Customer care

Answering the telephone ☐

Dealing with customer enquiries and complaints ☐

General conduct

Dress code ☐

Drinking/Drugs ☐

Personal hygiene ☐

Smoking ☐

Use of the telephone ☐

Health, safety and welfare issues

Company medical scheme ☐

Health surveillance ☐

Counselling ☐

Personal security and prevention of theft ☐

First aid ☐

Fire precautions ☐

Evacuation procedure ☐

Other emergency procedures ☐

Appendix B Training plan – pro forma

Employee name	Position held	Training need	Training methodology	Priority	Estimated duration and cost	Target completion date

Period covered by the plan   Employee grades covered ....

From .... to ....

Appendix C Versatility chart – pro forma

	Operation 1	Operation 2	Operation 3	Operation 4	Operation 5	Operation 6	Operation 7	Operation 8	Operation 9	Operation 10	Operation 11
Employee 1											
Employee 2											
Employee 3											
Employee 4											
Employee 5											
Employee 6											

Key

◆ Partly trained

✔ Fully trained

Appendix D Succession plan – pro forma

Function	Total	16	17	18	19	20	21	22	23	24	25–9	30–4	35–9	40–4	45–9	50–4	55	56	57	58	59	60

Appendix E
Programme evaluation – end-of-course questionnaire

Title of Course _____

Dates _____

Course tutor _____

Introduction

It would be greatly appreciated if you could complete the following questionnaire on the course that you have just attended. As well as providing your comments on individual sessions, we would like your views on the overall balance and cohesiveness of the course together with comments on some general issues.

PLEASE READ THROUGH THE WHOLE QUESTIONNAIRE BEFORE ANSWERING INDIVIDUAL QUESTIONS.

We would like you to rate the sessions on both *content* and *presentation* using a FIVE POINT scale as follows:

Content

1 = much too superficial/far too complex etc. to 5 = very useful/highly interesting/ pitched at just the right level etc. A score of THREE indicates general satisfaction overall, whilst leaving scope for improvement.

Presentation

1 = very poor communication/illegible visual aids/objectives not explained etc. to 5 = absorbing/very entertaining/excellent use of visual aids/objectives clearly explained etc. A score of THREE indicates that the content was put across satisfactorily, whilst leaving scope for improvement.

Any sessions not attended should be clearly marked N/A.

Thank you for your co-operation.

Name _____

Topic			Rating *(please tick)*										Comments
			Content					Presentation					*(if any)*
			Unsatisfactory ↔ excellent					Unsatisfactory ↔ excellent					
Session Title	Lecturer	1	2	3	4	5	1	2	3	4	5		
1.													
2.													
3.													
4.													
5.													
6.													
7.													
8.													
9.													
10.													
11.													
12.													
13.													
14.													
15.													
16.													
17.													
18.													
19.													
20.													

Please indicate on the scales provided the extent to which you agree with the following statements, adding additional comments if appropriate:

Comments (if any)

The objectives of the course were clearly explained

Strongly disagree	Disagree	Neutral	Agree	Strongly agree

The course was well balanced and logical in sequence

Strongly disagree	Disagree	Neutral	Agree	Strongly agree

There was a good balance of presentations and case studies/syndicate work

Strongly disagree	Disagree	Neutral	Agree	Strongly agree

Audio-visual materials were of good quality

Strongly disagree	Disagree	Neutral	Agree	Strongly agree

Pre-course reading materials were helpful

Strongly disagree	Disagree	Neutral	Agree	Strongly agree

The course notes contained useful information to support the lecturers

Strongly disagree	Disagree	Neutral	Agree	Strongly agree

The time allowed for case studies was adequate

Strongly disagree	Disagree	Neutral	Agree	Strongly agree

The time allowed for private study was adequate

Strongly disagree	Disagree	Neutral	Agree	Strongly agree

Refreshment breaks were well timed

Strongly disagree	Disagree	Neutral	Agree	Strongly agree

Lecture room facilities were good

Strongly disagree	Disagree	Neutral	Agree	Strongly agree

Where applicable, accommodation was comfortable

Strongly disagree	Disagree	Neutral	Agree	Strongly agree

The course has been interesting and rewarding

Strongly disagree	Disagree	Neutral	Agree	Strongly agree

Additional comments

References

Advisory Committee on the Safety of Nuclear Installations (1993) *Study Group on Human Factors, Third Report, Organising for Safety*, HMSO.

Asda Stores (1994) *Asda Health and Safety: Your Personal Guide*, Asda Stores Ltd., Leeds.

Booth, R.T. (1994) *Measuring Health and Safety Performance – An Overview*, Aston University Lecture.

Cooper, M.J. (1995) 'A study of the quality of open training materials supplied to the engineering industry', *Journal of European Industrial Training*, **19**(2).

Hale, A.R. and Glendon, A.I. (1987) *Individual Behaviour in the Control of Danger*, Amsterdam: Elsevier.

Harrison, R. (1989) *Training and Development*, London: Institute of Personnel Management.

HSE (1997) *Successful Health and Safety Management*, HS(G)65, Health and Safety Executive.

Rasmussen, J., Duncan, K. and Leplat, J. (eds.) (1974) *New Technology and Human Error*, Chichester: Wiley.

Reason, J.T. (1990) *Human Error*, Cambridge University Press.

Safety and Health at Work (1972) Report of the Committee, 1970-72, Committee on Safety and Health at Work, Cmnd 5034, HMSO.

Training Agency (1989) *Training in Britain – A Study of Funding, Activity and Attitudes*, HMSO.